THE DARK ARTS

Earnest Spellbinder

Scripture Union

Copyright © Catherine Butcher 2002
First published 2002

Scripture Union, 207–209 Queensway, Bletchley,
Milton Keynes, MK2 2EB, England.

ISBN 1 85999 471 7

All rights reserved. No part of this publication may be reproduced, stored in a retrieval system, or transmitted in any form or by any means, electronic, mechanical, photocopying, recording or otherwise, without the prior permission of Scripture Union.

The right of Catherine Butcher to be identified as author of this work has been asserted by her in accordance with the Copyright, Designs and Patents Act 1988.

Scripture taken from the HOLY BIBLE, NEW INTERNATIONAL VERSION. Copyright © 1973, 1978, 1984 by International Bible Society. Used by permission of Hodder and Stoughton Limited.

All illustrations by Colin Smithson.

Additional research by Caroline Kimber.

British Library Cataloguing-in-Publication Data.
A catalogue record of this book is available from the British Library.

Printed and bound in Great Britain by Creative Print and Design (Wales) Ebbw Vale.

Scripture Union is an international Christian movement working with children, young people and families in more than 130 countries around the world.

For Rachel and Matthew

I have put together this book from manuscripts taken from the Babylonian Academy for Training Sorcerers before the Great Fire destroyed the city of Babylon. The stories match those found in the Old Testament book of Daniel accepted by Jews, Christians and many archaeologists. Some ancient treasures relating to the story can still be found in the British Museum.

The diary found in the manuscripts was written by a student of witchcraft and wizardry. It has been kept in the restricted section of the library and no student has had access to it... until now! It has been used for reference by staff and, in particular, by professors teaching protection against the dark arts. Now this new edition is being made available to all. It speaks of powers that are much greater than any magician can use.

I have added my notes throughout to help readers who haven't got my academic background and insight into Babylonian and Hebrew history.

Earnest Spellbinder

Chapter 1

Note from Earnest Spellbinder

This is taken from the Diary of Memet – a student and then a professor in the Magician's House at the Babylonian Academy for Training Sorcerers (BATS for short).

Day 1

The victory parade was massive. We could see the cloud of dust on the horizon long before anyone reached the gates of Babylon. "Boom, boom, crash, crash, boom." The rhythmic thundering of hundreds of marching feet and giant ceremonial drums made the city walls shudder. The Babylonian army were dressed in red with belts round their waists and ornate turbans on their heads. Each warrior was carrying something gold. We didn't know what they were but word quickly spread round the crowd:

"They're gold plates and goblets from Jerusalem."

"The army have destroyed the Hebrew kingdom."

"They smashed their holy temple!"

"They captured their royal family!"

"Victory for Babylon!"

"Scum, scum, Hebrew scum!" We all chanted in time to the drum beats at the group of prisoners who were following the marching soldiers. But these royal prisoners weren't like the miserable crowd I've seen before. They were proud and tall. "Gorgeous hunks" was what the girls from Enchanters called them! Girls! Typical! I could see them fluttering their eyelashes like they always do with boys they fancy. Made me want to puke!

Old Ash-face (Ashpenaz, the King's chief court official) fussed around the prisoners like a mother hen. Zeth, one of the Sorcerers, heard him talking to the Commander of the Guard, "The prisoners are from the Israelite royal family. King Nebuchadnezzar has ordered that the best looking and brightest of the bunch should be brought back as prisoners." I was gobsmacked when Ash ushered four of the prisoners through the school gates and into an empty house in the courtyard.

"Must be some mistake," said Big and Biz (two other Magicians). "What's going on?" they asked Ash later. "Shouldn't you escort them straight to jail – do not pass go, do not collect 200 silver pieces?" Ash, his chest pushed out with pride, turned to face them and announced, so most of us could hear, "His royal majesty, the mighty King Nebuchadnezzar, has chosen me, Ashpenaz, chief of his court officials, to teach the prisoners our language and literature. After three years here with us at the Babylonian Academy for Training Sorcerers, benefitting from my wisdom and understanding, they will enter the king's service." Although he didn't say

it, he obviously thought the rest of us would never pass our final exams.

Day 2

This morning a notice went up on the door of the prisoners' house. Ash-face had written a self-important note announcing the prisoners' new Babylonian names. We all crowded round to have a look.

> The prisoner formerly known as Daniel will be called Belteshazzar (that's after King Neb's favourite god Bel, not to be confused with that layabout Prince Belshazzar); Hananiah will be known as Shadrach (what a joke – it means something like "I am very fearful"); Mishael will be Meshach (another joke – it means "I'm a nobody") and Azariah will be Abednego ("I'm a servant of the god Nego").

I thought we should have had one of the foreigners in each of the four houses – the Enchanters would have eaten them alive – but Ash decided to keep them together in their own house so he could coach them. I don't see how they can catch up with us fourth years, especially if they're not hot on our language.

By lunchtime, when we saw them next, they were all kitted out in robes, turbans and baggy trousers like the rest of us – why can't we wear black cloaks like other wizarding schools?

Earnest Spellbinder's note about witches and pointy hats

You can't tell who's a witch by what they wear. Black pointy hats are part of the Welsh national costume and were standard dress in medieval times! Old women with warty noses aren't all witches either. Witches, wizards or warlocks try to tap into spiritual powers to work magic or spells. The Bible first mentions witchcraft about 3,500 years ago, together with people who make human sacrifices, cast spells or try to speak with the dead, interpret omens or practice divination (interpreting omens and divination are supposed to be ways of discovering the future supernaturally).

When the prisoners arrived in the dining room with their guard, the whole hall fell silent – it was as if a tongue-tying curse had worked for once. The foreigners sat down at a table between Astrologers and Sorcerers and the usual bustle began again. The tables were laden with plates of meat in delicious sauces and bowls of ornately carved vegetables – Big and Biz had their usual fight over the vegetables which were carved like little gods. Eating is one of the favourite occupations of Magicians so we quickly forgot about the foreigners.

But heads soon turned when Ash-face started another flap. The most regal-looking of the prisoners was sitting with his arms folded not eating. "It's a hunger strike," Zeth hissed. The tall prisoner leant over and whispered to Ash, who went as grey as gruel. They seemed to be having an argument – Ash was using

frantic sign language to say the king would chop his head off.

Zeth told me later that the foursome had asked permission not to eat our food (students at BATS eat food directly from the King's table after it has

Earnest Spellbinder's note about salt

Know the difference between right and left? Some people in the Middle Ages believed it could be the difference between life and death. Salt was a precious thing, symbolic of life itself. People thought that angels whispered in your right ear and the devil in your left. Spilling salt meant you were spilling life, and that gave the devil a chance to whisper to you! To defend yourself you threw salt over your left shoulder, throwing salt in the devil's face.

been offered to his gods.) They wanted vegetables instead! Big and Biz must have heard what was said, as they had shot across the dining hall like sparks from a sorcerer's staff to grab the plates of unwanted food.

Ash replaced the prisoners' food with plain, uncarved veg and no sauce – not even ketchup! We all had glasses of pumpkin wine, but they had water. I saw Biz staring at them as he shovelled forkfuls of grub into his enormous mouth, bits of pumpkin pie and cream dribbling down his wobbling chin. "They won't keep that up," he spluttered between mouthfuls. "They'll look like gangly gerbils by the end of the week."

Day 12

Biz had to eat his words today. After ten days of veg and water, the prisoners took our last SWAT (Standard Wizards Academic Test) in the morning and Professor Poultice came over from the hospital wing to give them a thorough physical check-up. When we arrived for lunch, Ash stood up and read out a notice:

> Following stringent mental and physical tests, the young Israelite men have proved that their vegetable diet is healthier than our Babylonian fare. By decree of his royal majesty, as from this day, all pupils at BATS will eat the Israelite diet. Wine and the King's food will be reserved for feast days.

Big and Biz let out a long moan. Later I saw them trying to bribe two sixth-form boys to conjure up a bacon sandwich. Astrologers Caspar and Melchior began stockpiling whatever extra food they could find. Midnight feasts look set to become serious events after today.

Earnest Spellbinder's note about astrology

Astrologers claim to interpret the influence that stars and planets have on people. Many people read their horoscope to find out what's going to happen to them. However, only God knows the future – the same God who made the stars in the first place. Don't get confused with astronomy – the scientific study of stars, planets and things whizzing around in space.

Day 13

I'm getting to know the Hebrews a bit better. Shadrach, Meshach and Abednego stick together and seem quite chatty – they already knew some of our language before they were captured. Belteshazzar's not so easy-going, he keeps his distance. He never answers to his Babylonian name so most of us are calling him Daniel – that's what his friends call him – Daniel the dream-reader.

They are not getting it all their own way after the food fiasco. Professor Carshena gave them extra homework for refusing to touch animal entrails in divination. Professor Harbona kept them in for an hour after school when they refused to cast spells – they just announced a blessing or a curse – it's as if their words simply flesh out. Potty Purves in Distillation, Infusion and Mixing class (DIM for short) gave them top marks when they could recite all the recipes perfectly and they opted out of Transmogrification to take more time to study their scrolls. I've heard they are already pretty good at Iconology. Can't wait to see what they do in Horticulture and Hydrography classes. We're working on the Hanging Gardens of Babylon tomorrow. I've heard them singing about a "fountain of life". Let's see what they make of the most magnificent wonder of the modern world.

Day 68

All that extra homework and detention seems to have paid off for the foreign foursome. When

Earnest Spellbinder's note about spelling

Is spelling your least favourite school subject? Did you know the word 'spell' you use in Literacy lessons has the same origins as a magic 'spell'? Words are powerful. Using them wrongly – like calling someone names – can have lasting effects.

King Neb held the final oral exam, they came top of Year Four. In just one term they have caught up with the best of us. In fact, when the annual report was posted on the school gate, Ash underlined the bit that said:

In every matter of wisdom and understanding about which the king questioned them, the

Israelites were ten times better than all the Magicians and Enchanters in the whole kingdom.

Ash strutted round like a peacock for days after that.

Chapter 2

Note from Earnest Spellbinder

It is now a number of years later. Memet has obviously become a teacher at BATS and has started another diary.

Day 55
Today was the worst day of my life. We'd taken our students on an overnight field trip to the Tower of Babel with the Astrologers. Stargazing's much better without the city lights – the sky is blacker than a magician's cloak. Even though the Tower of Babel's in ruins, it's still the tallest building in the world.

As the sun came up we headed back to the city. "Can't wait for bed," said Caspar as we rode our camels through the gates. "I'm ready for a good sleep."

Suddenly we were surrounded by armed guards. "These are Astrologers!" one shouted triumphantly. "Yep, and some Magicians. The King wants you," said another, sounding as if he'd just found the latest delicacy for the lions' den.

Caspar and his classmates looked as if the snake-headed monsters on the city gates had come to life. Melchior began to sob. My knees turned to jelly. What would the king want *us* for? Had he heard about the plague of frogs experiment we'd been trying?

Earnest Spellbinder's note about alchemy

Centuries ago chemistry lessons would have been called alchemy classes. Alchemists wanted to do two things: to change cheap metals into gold to become rich and to find the elixir of life – a medicine thought to make you live forever.

The palace corridors were vast. Alabaster statues looked down their long noses at us as we scurried past. The great hall was packed with almost every magician, enchanter, sorcerer and astrologer in the land. You could cut the silence with a sword.

Then the king spoke, "I have had a dream that troubles me and I want to know what it means."

"O king, live forever! Tell your servants the dream, and we will interpret it," said Balthazar, the chief astrologer.

But the king wasn't having it. He'd got it into his head that if the astrologers and magicians couldn't tell him what his dream was, they weren't worth having. What does he think we are? Mind readers?!

I was so busy saying how impossible the task was that I nearly missed what the king said next. "If you do not tell me what my dream was AND interpret it, I will have you cut into pieces and your houses turned into piles of rubble."

I was terrified. Why had I wanted to be a magician? I'd rather be a marsh-fisherman or maybe a glass-maker. I don't want to die!

At the front of the vast hall, Balthazar was daring to talk back to the king. "Tell us the dream..." he snivelled.

"No, I will not!" shouted the king furiously, his fist crashing down on the arm of his golden throne.

"No man on earth can do what the king asks! No one can reveal a dream except the gods, and they do not live among men," Balthazar whimpered.

"The gods certainly don't seem very talkative these days," I thought. "I can't remember a single twitch or whisper from their stony faces." But the last thing Balthazar said rang a bell for me. "The gods do not live among men..."

Daniel always talked about his God as if he was on friendly terms with him. But no time to think. There was a flash of steel and we were surrounded. "Execute the lot of them!" said the king, and my stomach did a horrible somersault.

The Commander of the Guard had no choice. He sent soldiers to round up the last few magicians ready for the execution to begin. As Daniel was brought in I heard him ask, "Why did the king issue such a harsh decree?" The Commander muttered a few words, then Daniel turned on his heel and marched boldly up to the front of the crowd.

"Give me some time and the God of Heaven will give me the interpretation of your dream, O king."

Everyone froze. Silent.

"You can have one night. If you cannot return with the interpretation when the cock crows in the morning, you and all that so-called psychic rabble will die."

Daniel bowed and backed away. Shadrach, Meshach and Abednego joined him and the sea of magicians and sorcerers parted to let them leave the room.

Day 56

Last night we couldn't sleep. We could hear the muffled voices of Daniel and his three friends pleading for mercy from the God of Heaven. I know lots of gods – gods of trees and wood, fire and water – but this God of Daniel's was new to me. Why ask the God of Heaven for mercy? What's he got to do with this?

We were up long before dawn. No one could eat so much as a pistachio nut. Sneaking out, I peered through the window of the Israelite house and there were Daniel, Shadrach, Meshach and Abednego talking to their God as if he was in the room with them.

Earnest Spellbinder's note about crossing fingers

People cross their fingers because they think it brings good luck. It is a superstition linked to the belief that the cross of Jesus is powerful. The cross was Jesus's way to show us his love and point us to life forever with him. Crossing your fingers doesn't do anything magical! Crosses mean lots of things: a cross on your homework means you're wrong; a cross on a letter means you're loved; and a cross on a map means there's hidden treasure!

As the cock crowed, Daniel started singing. It was something about God, "Wisdom and power are his ... he sets up kings and deposes them ... he gives wisdom to the wise (does that mean he's got the interpretation of the dream?) ... he reveals deep and hidden things (surely he must know) ..." Then Daniel said, "I thank and praise you, God of my fathers, you have made known to us the dream of the king."

"YES! We're saved!" I ran back to the other Magicians shouting the news to anyone who'd listen. We all crowded round the Israelite house. When the Commander arrived with the guards, everyone went quiet. We would still be for the chop if Daniel was wrong.

When the kitchen cat walked past, some of the Astrologers yelped and said it was a bad omen. A group of Sorcerers had used blood from a rat

Earnest Spellbinder's note about black cats

Superstitions about cats could leave you tied up in knots! Some believe you'll have bad luck if a black cat crosses your path, others say it is lucky. Yet another 'school' believes that if the cat comes towards you, it brings luck. If you stroke the cat the luck is transferred to you and if the cat walks off it is taking the luck away!

Earnest Spellbinder's note about blood

Spilling blood has serious consequences, quite apart from the possibility of death! When Hebrew slaves painted blood on their doorposts about 3,500 years ago, the Angel of Death passed over their homes (Read about it in the Bible book of Exodus chapter 12 verse 23). Jews still mark this supernatural event today all over the world when they celebrate Passover.

to perform a protection spell. Big and Biz were trying to remember an incantation to turn themselves into birds so they could fly away.

But Daniel was completely calm. "Do not execute the wise men of Babylon. Take me to the king and I will interpret the dream for him." Off they went, the points of the soldiers' swords clipping the stones, making an eerie clanking sound as they marched off to the palace.

It seemed like hours before anything happened. Then click, click, clickety-click, we heard the guards' swords clipping the stones again, coming closer and closer.

Everyone trembled as the soldiers marched back though the gates. Cunning, as always, the Sorcerers thought they could bribe their way out. The Enchanters barricaded themselves into their house and surrounded it with mirrors "to ward off evil". But the guards marched straight over to Daniel's house and went in. We didn't know what to think.

Soon they came back out, carrying boxes of parchment and a few old robes. They even took

Earnest Spellbinder's note about mirrors

Can you see a person's soul? Some people think the reflection of a person in a mirror is their soul, so breaking the mirror brings bad luck. Some even think it brings seven years of bad luck unless you bury the fragments. If you believe that God is in control of the world and nothing happens by chance, then there's no such thing as luck!

down the tiny box of Hebrew scriptures that Daniel had fixed on the doorpost.* Then they were gone. The next thing we knew Ashpenaz appeared with a circle of blue parchment, which he nailed to the door. It read:

Daniel, Ruler of the
Entire Province of Babylon
lived here, together with
Shadrach, Meshach and Abednego –
Administrators of the Province. During
their stay they were under the sole
care and guidance of Ashpenaz, chief
of the king's court officials, who
was responsible for teaching
them everything they know.

Ashpenaz the Arrogant we called him after that. But what did it all mean? Daniel, Ruler of the Entire Province of Babylon? It wasn't long before we found out. Ash was keen to tell everyone he met.

"The king asked Daniel to tell him the dream and what it meant. I nearly fainted when Daniel replied, "No wise man, enchanter, magician or diviner can explain the king's dream," but then he said, "there is a God in heaven who reveals mysteries.""

** Earnest Spellbinder: Jewish people still do this today to show how important their Scriptures are.*

"Then Daniel began to explain the dream just as if it had been his own. He emphasised that he was no wiser than other men but that it was his God who had revealed the dream."

Ash drew a quick sketch in the sand to show us what the king had dreamt. He drew an awesome statue with a head made of pure gold. It had a silver chest and arms and a bronze belly and thighs. Its legs were made of iron and its feet were made of clay mixed with iron.

"Daniel described a rock 'cut out, but not by human hands'. It struck the statue's feet and smashed them. Everything else crumbled to dust and was blown away. The rock that hit the statue became a huge mountain and filled the whole earth.

"King Neb nodded enthusiastically. Daniel had got it right. But even though he knew the dream, it wasn't easy to explain," Ash said. "But Daniel knew what it meant."

"He said the statue was like a time line of empires. Babylon was at the top and King Neb was the head of gold, the king of kings. But, as usual, Daniel reserved the highest praise for his God, the King of Heaven. No one knew how King Neb would take it when Daniel said, "*The King of Heaven* has given you power and glory". Daniel gave his God all the credit for Neb's greatness!*

** Earnest Spellbinder: Take a look at Daniel chapter 2 to find out what happened next.*

Chapter 3

Day 120
Daniel's vision has gone to the king's head. Not content with being the head of gold, he wants to have a kingdom that will last forever. At least that's how I see it.

Ever since the dream, the king has had a secret project out on the plain of Dura. The rumour is that the king has mastered some dark magic and is planning to fly to the moon. There was certainly a lot of smoke from the giant smelting furnaces being used nearby.

When the project finally went public, it was laughable really. King Neb had commissioned a giant golden statue – sixty cubits high and six cubits wide*. I think it was supposed to be a statue of the king as a god – though it was more like a giant golden banana.

Royal heralds were sent out to summon the king's advisers to the dedication of the statue. The decree said, "As soon as you hear the music play, you must bow down and worship the statue. Whoever does not fall down and worship will immediately be thrown into a blazing furnace."

It was like an enormous game of musical bumps. Only, instead of waiting for the music to stop before bumping down, all the top men in the

** Earnest Spellbinder: That's 27 metres high and 2.7 metres wide.*

land fell down in front of the statue as soon as the royal orchestra struck its first note.

They had done it a few times when I saw Balthazar and some other astrologers heading for the king. “O king, live forever!” said Balthazar. And then he did a despicable thing. He said, “There are some Jews – Shadrach, Meshach and Abednego – who pay no attention to you, O king. They won’t worship your golden image.”

What a tell-tale. He must have been jealous of the dream-reading that had left him looking powerless. Everyone knew that the Israelites only worshipped the God of Heaven, but with their lives at stake what would they do?

Guards brought the threesome before the king. King Neb seemed to think he had the upper hand. “What god will be able to save you from ME!” he boomed. But Shadrach, Meshach and Abednego replied, “If we are thrown into the blazing furnace, the God we serve is able to save us from it. But even if he does not, we want you to know that we will not serve your gods or worship the image of gold you have set up.”

Naturally, King Neb was furious. Six of the strongest soldiers were ordered to tie up the trio and throw them into the nearest furnace. The flames were so hot that all six soldiers died as they threw Shadrach, Meshach and Abednego into the raging fire.

King Neb couldn’t resist the urge to watch them burn – he always had a cruel streak. As he bent down low to look into the furnace, he shouted out in amazement. “Look! There are

four men walking around in the fire. The fourth looks like a son of the gods!"

Suddenly the king was calling, "Shadrach, Meshach and Abednego, servants of the Most High God, come out! Come here!"

They did and they didn't even smell smoky. Their hair wasn't even singed. We were totally gobsmacked. "Who was with them in the furnace?" "Who'd use a portal that opened in a fire?" "Was it

Earnest Spellbinder's note about portals

Portals are ways of getting from one place to another. Star Trek characters use a teleporter to travel great distances quickly. Children visit C S Lewis's Narnia through a wardrobe. J K Rowling's wizards use a portkey. In Medieval times, marshes were thought to be a portal into the spirit world. Throughout the ages people have looked for ways to travel into other worlds.

a god?" "Might have been an apparition." Everyone was talking at once.

The king silenced everyone when he announced, "Praise the God of Shadrach, Meshach and Abednego, who has sent his angel and rescued his servants! They trusted in him and were willing to give up their lives rather than worship any god except their own God." Then he decreed, "Anyone who says anything against their God will be cut to pieces, for no other god can save in this way." He promoted the trio to an even higher rank and sent everyone back home. The guy's bananas!

Chapter 4

Day 428

We wise men were called on today by the new king. Well, when I say "king", the real king has been away for the past 12 years fighting battles, leaving his son Belshazzar in charge. He really is a lazy, good-for-nothing. Not like old King Neb from my young days. Our enemies have surrounded the city, but Belshazzar's too busy stuffing his face to bother defending the kingdom.

Today he held a banquet for a thousand of his nobles. It was a fantastic feast served on golden plates with ornate golden goblets for the wine. I thought I had seen those plates before and then I remembered. They were the treasures taken from the temple in Jerusalem all those years ago. The king must have been mad to use temple treasures.

Suddenly Belshazzar dropped his golden goblet and pointed to the wall. The fingers of a human hand were writing on the white plaster, but the hand wasn't connected to a body! Everyone was terrified! We could see the letters clearly in the lamplight. The king turned an unearthly shade of grey and slumped back into his chair, shaking like a leaf.

I've read about mischievous poltergeists creating mayhem. Was this a jinx or the handiwork of a ghost? The King shouted to the astrologers and magicians, promising a royal reward to anyone who could read the writing and

Earnest Spellbinder's note about ladders

Prop a ladder against a wall and it forms a triangle. The shape might please your Maths teacher but some people used to believe that walking under a ladder showed disrespect to the Trinity (God the Father, God the Son and God the Holy Spirit). But the bad luck is more about having a bucket fall on your head than about God!

Earnest Spellbinder's note about ghosts

Ghosts and poltergeists are thought to be the souls of dead people – but there is no proof that they have ever existed.

explain it. But the petrified sorcerers and magicians had no answers. The Queen Mother remembered that King Neb had appointed Daniel as chief of magicians. "Call for him and he will tell you what this writing means," she said.

When Daniel read the words, they sounded like a children's nursery rhyme, "Eeny meeny tickle a parson!" If only they *were* just a huge joke. Daniel translated them, "God has numbered the days of your reign and brought it to an end; you have been weighed on the scales and found wanting; your kingdom is divided and given to the Medes and Persians."*

** Earnest Spellbinder: The records show that Darius the Mede invaded Babylon that very night and Belshazzar was killed: Daniel's words came true. Look at Daniel chapter 5, verses 30 and 31.*

Earnest Spellbinder: At this point some of Memet's diaries have been lost as we catch up with him many years later in yet another diary...

Chapter 5

Day 999
Here we go again. Another king. A new court. Strange customs. It's all too hard for me at my age. Daniel just carries on as usual. Eating his plain food, praying three times a day, writing down as many of his scriptures as he can remember "for future generations".*

He doesn't seem bothered by court politics even though one of Darius's first decisions was to make him Prime Minister. The two deputy ministers and their followers are not pleased. There's a plot in the making. Jealousy and intrigue are in the air.

Day 1010
Spies are watching Daniel. Is he fiddling the books? Does he break the law? I know they're trying to catch him out, but I've been watching him for years. He never puts a foot wrong – it would be sickening, if he wasn't so likeable. He's easy to be with, always looking out for other people, clear about right and wrong, with no worries about life or death.

** Earnest Spellbinder: As a boy, Daniel would have learned much of what's called the Old Testament off by heart. It has been copied and handed down from one generation to the next and is still part of the Bible today.*

Day 1047

They've trapped Darius with his own pride, and they've got Daniel as well. It only took a little white lie. The deputies had an audience with King Darius today. "*All* your ministers have agreed," they said, lying through their teeth. Daniel hadn't even been consulted.

They had agreed that Darius should become "Defender of Faith". Everyone was to bow down to Darius not just as their king, but as a god. Naturally, it sounded good to Darius. Having one religion would unite the nation. What could be better? He signed the new law and added his seal. No one could refuse to obey unless they wanted to be fed to the lions.

Day 1050

The deputies' henchmen were waiting under Daniel's window when he opened it to pray today. As soon as they heard him talking to the "God of Heaven" they were off, bleating to the king, "Daniel's ignoring you." Immediately Darius knew he'd been tricked. He didn't want Daniel to die, but how could he get round his own law?

Earnest Spellbinder's note about jinxes

A jinx is a person or thing that brings bad luck. The 'jinx' on witches is they think they're in control of special powers. But when they try to stop using that power, they often find that the evil source of those powers is controlling them. Only God can help them break free from the jinx.

They came for Daniel just as I was dropping off to sleep. I heard the click, click, clickety-click of swords on cobbles. I threw on some clothes and followed, keeping my distance. They were taking Daniel to the royal zoo. I could hear the rumbling roar of the lions getting closer. They hadn't been fed all week.

Darius was standing by the entrance to the lions' den, wringing his hands. He looked genuinely sorry for making such a stupid law. "May your God, whom you serve continually, deliver you," he said softly, as Daniel was pushed into the outer chamber of the lions' den. A huge stone was rolled across the opening, sealing him in. The guards pulled the chains opening the gates to the lions' sleeping chamber and the roaring of lions became deafening. Darius left, looking very sick.

Day 1051

Was it my own snoring, or the lions that woke me? I had fallen asleep on a stone bench – not a good idea for someone my age. The king was back at dawn. He looked dreadful. He hadn't slept much either.

"Daniel," he called out. "Daniel, has your God saved you?" What was he thinking of? He'd seen the lions leaping up the sides of the pit, half starved, ready to pounce on anything edible.

Then I heard Daniel's voice. I thought I was going mad and hearing voices in my head. But there it was, clear as anything, "My God sent his angel and shut the lions' mouths. They have not hurt me."

Earnest Spellbinder's note about sacrifice

Making a sacrifice means giving up something valuable for the sake of someone else. From the times of early history, people have killed animals as a way of making a sacrifice to their gods. It is a way of saying "this is really important – important enough for something to die". When Jesus Christ was crucified, he became the sacrifice to end all sacrifices. That's why Christians don't sacrifice animals.

King Darius looked like a new man. "Get him out! Immediately!" he commanded and I rushed forward to help the king's bodyguard roll away the stone. We pulled Daniel out of the den and he looked as if he'd had a night's sleep in a luxury hotel. There wasn't a mark on him. I couldn't wait to ask him what the angel looked like.

Chapter 6

Day 2,529

I finally plucked up courage to talk to Daniel today. I've watched him over the years, since we were students together at BATS. Now we are both old men. Daniel has looked at the face of death but he never seems to be afraid. I've seen fellow magicians become like slaves to the powers they want to possess. Sometimes I feel special exploring the unknown magical world – but most of the time I'm afraid I'll unleash something I can't handle.

All my life, I've pursued the magician's goal to conquer death. Not just to possess the bodies of others, like the Sorcerers try to do, but to live forever. But Daniel is fearless and free, even though he came here as a captive. He's been in Babylon nearly 60 years now, but he still talks with certainty about the Israelites going home. I think he heard a prophecy when he was a young boy in Jerusalem. Maybe he has the secret to eternal life! I have so many questions.

I found Daniel sitting by the river, watching the stars. He doesn't look at the heavens like we Babylonians do. "Who needs to look at stars to know the future?" he said. "I know the God of Heaven. He created them and set each star in place. I can trust him to map out my future."

"How do you know the God of Heaven?" I asked.

"Haven't you heard that street preacher Ezekiel? What he says about God is true; God wants to change hard hearts and help us live his way. That's how you start to know him."*

"How can people have a total change of heart? That sounds impossible!"

"We are talking about the God of Heaven here: the creator of the universe. He is the God who revealed the kings' dreams to me. The one who sent a messenger to protect Shadrach, Meshach and Abednego in the fiery furnace and who protected me from those lions. He can do anything!

"Through all these years of talking to God, listening to him, reading the Scriptures, I've got to know him and how much he loves his followers. He has shown me glimpses of how my life fits into the big picture, why I am here and what he is like. All the amazing things that have happened in my life are because of God. He's given me a purpose and hope and I know he's more powerful than anything else."

"So that's why you weren't scared of the lions?"

"Of course! I knew God was in control, so how *could* I be afraid?"

When he put it like that, it made so much sense. But I had one more question I just had to ask. "But surely you fear death like everybody else? Or do you have the secret to eternal life?" I waited, holding my breath.

** Earnest Spellbinder: Look at Ezekiel 36:26 to hear what Ezekiel said about our hearts.*

Daniel smiled and looked over the river to the west. Eventually he spoke, "My people and I are looking forward to the day when we can go home to Jerusalem. It's in God's hands and we trust him. Why should we trust him any less about life and death? You can trust him with your future too."

"Even *I* can trust him? Me? A Babylonian?" I was astonished.

Suddenly it felt as if my heart was in my throat.

Friday and the number 13

Legend has it that Adam and Eve were expelled from the Garden of Eden on a Friday. The number 13 is supposed to be unlucky because there were 13 at the Last Supper and, as Jesus was crucified on a Friday, Friday and the number 13 means double trouble! (Read about Adam, Eve, the Last Supper and Jesus's crucifixion in the Bible.) It's odd how superstitions sometimes come from Christian beliefs that have got confused or muddled.

I wanted to be certain about the future like Daniel. I didn't want to be afraid of gods or kings or dark forces anymore. I wanted to know the true God.

"Where do I begin?" I asked.

"'Change my heart, God,' is a good prayer to start with. And when you do that, you'll find something else you've been looking for too. You'll soon find that God's perfect love will remove all your fear. Living God's way is the ultimate defence against the dark arts."

I didn't know if I could be as brave as Daniel but I knew I wanted to know his God. Today is the first day of the new me – Memet, Friend of God and Defender against the Dark Arts.

Note from Earnest Spellbinder

Here Memet's diary ends. He took the first step into a new life, more exciting than anything written here!

A final note from Earnest Spellbinder

Many students have asked me how they can know the power of God as Daniel did, so here are some pointers. The starting point is the same today as it has been since the dawn of time. We need to recognise that God is God, King of Kings and Lord of Lords. He's more powerful than any other powers or forces and more loving that anyone can imagine.

Because God is fair he doesn't let wrong go unpunished. But, because he is loving, he allowed someone else, Jesus Christ, to pay for the wrong things we do, protecting us from the consequences.

Jesus is described as a king but he was not like any other king. He didn't live in a palace. He had followers, but no troops or army. He was killed, but he came back to life even after he had been buried! At first, only a few people followed him, but today there are millions of people who believe in Jesus. Just like King Neb dreamed, "the rock" (as Jesus is sometimes called) destroyed a weak and divided kingdom and has spread into every country on earth.

Being God's follower is just as possible now as it was in Daniel's time. How amazing is that?

Jesus offers the ultimate protection against dark forces. That's why Paul, another of God's followers, was able to say, "I am convinced that neither death nor life, neither angels nor demons, neither the present nor the future, nor any powers... will be able to separate us from the love of God that is in Christ Jesus."

Being God's follower is a supernatural existence as well as being very practical. Like Daniel, you'll need training. He only had bits of the Bible to help him get to know God; the bits about Jesus hadn't been written then. Before you read the Bible, speak to God (it's called praying and ordinary words are fine) and ask him to help you understand what you read.

Expect God to speak to you. He spoke to Daniel in dreams. Scripture Union, who published this book, specialise in helping children and young people to be God's followers. You can also find help from Christians in a church near you or at a school club run by Christians. You could even write to me at Scripture Union to find out more!

Earnest Spellbinder
c/o Scripture Union Publishing
207-209 Queensway
Bletchley
Milton Keynes
MK2 2EB

Although Memet's diaries are a mythical history of life at the Babylonian Academy for Training Sorcerers, they are based on the real story of Daniel found in the Bible in the book of Daniel, chapters 1–6.

Daniel wrote around 535 BC, about the events taking place in Babylon from 605 BC until then.